RYA Recognised Training Centres

Published by
The Royal Yachting Association
RYA House Ensign Way Hamble
Southampton SO31 4YA
Tel: 0845 345 0400
Fax: 0845 345 0329
Email: info@rya.org.uk
Web: www.rya.org.uk

RYA NATIONAL SAILING SCHEME

How to find the right sailing course

Many sailing clubs are RYA recognised for offering tuition and if you like the idea of sailing in a club environment, a local club can be an excellent place to learn. Alternatively, you can choose a course at a professional school or learn to sail during your holiday in the UK or overseas.

The reputation of the RYA National Sailing Scheme has been built on high standards and good tuition. RYA Training Centres vary according to the sailing area available and the type of boats and level of tuition on offer. Whether you wish to learn to sail locally or improve your sailing on holiday, there should be an RYA Training Centre to suit you.

To select a course that will meet your needs, visit the RYA website for a list of sailing schools **www.rya.org.uk** or call the RYA **023 8062 7400** for a free training centres' brochure.

Some RYA Training Centres have specialised facilities (including special boats) for people with disabilities. Others can offer integrated courses in standard boats. Some students with disabilities may need additional help to complete the full requirements for an RYA certificate. There is provision within the Scheme for certificates to be endorsed as appropriate. Please contact the Principal of your selected RYA Training Centre or the RYA for more information.

Sailors who want to go keelboat cruising should consider taking an RYA Day Skipper Practical Course. The RYA National Sailing Scheme covers small boats only and is not intended as a substitute for the RYA Cruising Scheme.

What is an RYA recognised Training centre?

Safety is a priority for the RYA. Each RYA Training Centre is regularly inspected for standards of tuition, facilities and equipment, as laid down by the RYA Training Division and published in the guidance notes. All must have qualified staff, suitable boats and adequate safety cover. RYA Training Centres should display a Certificate of Recognition specifying the activities for which they are recognised. They are also required to carry public liability insurance.

For beginners' courses (Levels 1 & 2) run in single-handed dinghies, there should be one instructor to a maximum of 6 students, or 1 to 3 in crewed dinghies with the instructor on board. Keelboat courses can be run with an instructor student ratio of up to 1 to 5 depending on the type of boat.

Training carried out in coastal conditions that are not tidal should include the tidal material in the Onshore Teaching section.

At the end of your course, the Principal or Chief Instructor will decide whether certificates are to be awarded. Certificates are specific to the type of boat used, ie dinghy, keelboat or multihull. If the Principal decides that further practice is necessary before awarding you a certificate, they will explain the reasons to you. Should you feel it necessary to appeal against the outcome, contact RYA Training for guidance.

RYA NATIONAL SAILING SCHEME

The courses

All the courses in the RYA National Sailing Scheme can be completed in just two days. Most are flexible and often available as evening or half day sessions.

Once at Level 2 standard sailors can choose any advanced module. Depending on experience it may be advisable to complete them in a particular order e.g. at some locations Seamanship Skills would be advisable as the next step.

Direct assessments

Experienced sailors may wish to have direct assessment of their skills rather than taking part in a training course. The criteria are outlined in this book. Individual items will be signed off by the assessing instructor and the declaration signed by the Principal or Chief Instructor.

What next?

After taking your course you may consider joining a club, or buying a boat and joining the class association, who organise a variety of events. The RYA website is a good place to find a club or locate your class association. **www.rya.org.uk.**

How to become an instructor

Having learnt to sail, you may enjoy passing your skills on to others. The RYA Instructor is an experienced sailor who has successfully completed a brief sailing test (the pre-entry test) and an instructor training course. RYA Instructors should also hold a first aid certificate and the RYA Powerboat Level 2 Certificate. Full details are contained in RYA publication G14, The Dinghy Coaching Handbook.

Courses for young people

The RYA offers a training scheme for young people, the Youth Sailing Scheme. Full details are published in RYA book G11. Following completion of the Youth Sailing Scheme, young people may participate in further training through the advanced modules of the National Sailing Scheme.

Windsurfing, Powerboating, Sail and Power Cruising

The RYA organises similar training schemes for all these activities. Full details are available from the website or RYA training.

Learning Resources

The RYA produces a wide range of materials to help you learn, from course handbooks to training videos. These can be obtained through RYA Training Centres and the RYA website or simply phone the RYA and ask for this free catalogue.

International Sailing Schools Association
Association Internationale des Ecoles de Voile
Internationale Zeilscholen Verenging
Internationale Segelschulen-Vereinigung

Start Sailing
Level 1

This course provides a short introduction to sailing for novices. By the end of the course, participants will have a basic understanding of boat handling techniques and background knowledge. It is recommended that all participants consolidate this short introduction with the *Basic Skills Level 2* course.

Tuition is provided by trained instructors, using appropriate supervision ratios as defined on page 3 of this logbook. Students will be kept informed of their individual progress throughout the course.

Section A
Practical

Rigging
Has wind awareness. Knowledge of spars and rigging, parts of the sail, sail controls and foils

> *Instructor's signature*

Ropework
Can tie a figure of eight knot, round turn and two half hitches and secure a rope to a cleat

> *Instructor's signature*

Sailing techniques and manoeuvres
Has wind awareness

Has a practical understanding of the following manoeuvres:

Reaching - sailing across the wind

Stopping - lying-to

Controlling speed

Tacking - turning the front of the boat through the wind

Getting out of irons

Sailing upwind

Sailing downwind

Gybing - turning the back of the boat through the wind

> *Instructor's signature*

Launching and recovery*
Can secure boat on trolley

Understands the principles of:

Wheeling a trolley clear of other boats and overhead cables

Launching and leaving the shore

Coming ashore and recovery of boat

Wind awareness ashore

> *Instructor's signature*

Section B
Sailing Background

Sailing theory and background
Has awareness of other water users

Has basic knowledge of rules of road - power versus sail, port versus starboard, overtaking boat, windward boat

Clothing and Equipment
Knows importance of personal buoyancy

Instructor's signature

Meteorology
Has awareness of onshore and offshore winds

Knows sources of weather information

Instructor's signature

Capsize recovery*
Understands basic theory (dry land capsize) and importance of staying with boat

Instructor's signature

Keelboat sailors only

Man overboard recovery
Understands action to be taken to recover a man overboard

Instructor's signature

Clothing and equipment
Understands use of safety harnesses if fitted

Instructor's signature

Emergency equipment and precautions
Awareness of potential hazards of fuel and gas

Has knowledge of stowage and use of fire extinguishers

Instructor's signature

Experienced sailor's direct assessment

The candidate will satisfactorily complete all of Section A and shall, afloat and ashore, satisfactorily answer questions on Section B

Chief Instructor's signature

*Not necessarily applicable to keelboats

Basic Skills Level 2

On completion of this course, the successful sailor will be safety conscious, have a basic knowledge of sailing and be capable of sailing without an instructor on board in light winds. It will be assumed that every student starting this course has already mastered the practical skills and absorbed the background knowledge required for *Start Sailing Level 1*. Both courses can be combined.

Tuition will be given by trained instructors, using appropriate supervision ratios as defined on page 3 of this logbook.

In dinghies or multihulls, capsize recovery will be conducted in a controlled manner, one boat at a time, with a suitable rescue boat in attendance.

The students' knowledge and ability will be assessed on a continuous basis, though an oral interview or short written paper may be used as the basis for theory assessment if required. Students will be kept informed of their individual progress throughout the course.

Section A
Practical

Rigging
Understands how to rig according to weather conditions

Able to reef ashore*

> *Instructor's signature*

Ropework
Can tie a bowline, clove hitch, reef knot and rolling hitch

> *Instructor's signature*

Sailing techniques and manoeuvres
Has basic practical understanding of the following:

The Five Essentials - sail setting, balance, trim, course made good and centreboard*

Leaving and returning to a beach, jetty or mooring

Coming alongside a moored boat

Knows basic rules of the road: power/sail, port/starboard, windward boat, overtaking boat

Aware of lee shore dangers, sailing in close company with others and man overboard recovery

> *Instructor's signature*

Launching and recovery*
Has knowledge of boat storage ashore, launching and recovery*

Able to paddle a sailing dinghy and row a boat around a short triangular course, come alongside and make fast†

> *Instructor's signature*

7

Capsize recovery

Has practical experience of one method of righting a
boat and knowledge of at least one other method

`Instructor's signature`

Racing

Understands the course and starting procedure
(May be covered as onshore teaching)

`Instructor's signature`

Multihull sailors only

Sailing techniques and manoeuvres

Understands the basic principles of crew weight,
airflow, technique (C.A.T.)

`Instructor's signature`

Keelboat sailors only

Rigging
Can reef afloat

`Instructor's signature`

Ropework
Can use winches

`Instructor's signature`

Use of engine (if fitted)
Has knowledge of engine checks, starting, stopping
and running procedures

Able to come alongside and pick up a mooring

`Instructor's signature`

Section B
Sailing Background

Sailing theory and background
Has knowledge of:

Points of sailing and No Go Zone

How a sail works - basic aerodynamic theory

Sea sailing - basic advice for inland sailors
including taking local advice. Tide tables, tidal
sequence of springs and neaps, ebb and flow

The effect of wind direction and tidal flow on
sailing conditions

Speed over the ground with/against tidal flow

Estuaries and harbour mouths - conditions and
hazards

Informing someone ashore

Inland sailing - basic advice including local bylaws,
permits, overhead power lines, locks and weirs

continued over

The dangers of hypothermia and the importance of first aid training, particularly cardio pulmonary resuscitation

Instructor's signature

Meteorology
Knows sources of weather and shipping forecasts, when to reef

Understands Beaufort Wind Scale

Instructor's signature

Clothing and equipment
Knows importance of personal safety, clothing and buoyancy, boat buoyancy and basic equipment depending on type of boat (may include anchor, paddle, bucket, bilge pump)

Instructor's signature

Emergency equipment and precautions
Knows importance of first aid kit and flares including stowage. Visual methods of attracting attention, action to help those in distress

Instructor's signature

Section C
Coastal (optional)

Capable of practical application of Section A in coastal waters

Able to anchor, (keelboats only) sail using transits

Understands how to apply weather forecasts in coastal waters

Instructor's signature

Section D
Experienced sailor's direct assessment

The candidate must present logged evidence of at least one full season's sailing experience. He will satisfactorily complete all of Section A and while afloat and ashore, satisfactorily answer questions on Section B. Candidates seeking assessment on coastal waters will demonstrate a proper knowledge of Section C

Chief Instructor's signature

*Not necessarily applicable to keelboats

†Not necessarily applicable to multihulls

Seamanship Skills

On completion of this course, the successful sailor will be capable of manoeuvring a dinghy/keelboat/multihull in a seamanlike manner and making seamanship decisions in moderate conditions.

It will be assumed that every student starting this course has already mastered the practical skills and absorbed the background knowledge required for *Basic Skills Level 2*.

Tuition will be given by trained instructors, using appropriate supervision ratios with regard to the location and competence of the students. Much of the work afloat will be done without an instructor aboard. The emphasis is on increasing the self reliance and decision making of the sailor.

Students will be informed of their individual progress throughout the course.

Section A
Practical

Ropework
Can tie a fisherman's bend and sheet bend

Can do heat sealing and whipping

Launching and recovery
Can leave and return to beach, jetty or mooring, including windward and leeward shore

Sailing techniques and manoeuvres
Is able to:

Heave to

Reef afloat

Recover man overboard

Be towed by a power vessel

Anchor, including principles and techniques for different circumstances†

Sail backwards

Sail in adverse circumstances (no rudder, no centreboard)* †

Knows how to prepare road trailer and secure trailer ashore

Section B
Sailing Background

Sailing theory and background
Understands the following terminology:

windward, leeward, abeam, forward, aft, ahead, astern, to weather, downwind, amidships, quarter, pinching, sailing by the lee, luff, bear away, planing, sternway, broaching

Knows and can apply the following International Regulations for the Prevention of Collisions at Sea (IRPCS):

meeting other sailing vessels, meeting power driven vessels, following or crossing narrow channels, action by stand-on vessel

Instructor's signature

Capsize recovery
Knows how to recover from total inversion (practical session if possible)

Instructor's signature

Meteorology
Knows sources of information on weather patterns for the day

Can interpret forecasts and understand local effects

Aware of Beaufort Wind Scale and changing weather conditions, including fog

Instructor's signature

Section C
Coastal - optional

Capable of practical application of Section A on coastal waters

Can use local tide tables

Understands rate of rise and fall - Twelfth's Rule. Is aware of tidal streams

Has a basic understanding of charts and important symbols

Instructor's signature

Section D
For keel boat sailors

Desirable but not essential items
Understands the importance of:

Inspection of slipway and overhead clearance

Use of rope between trailer and vehicle

Recovery: use of guide poles

Use of crane/derrick including slings and
weight distribution

Instructor's signature

Experienced sailor's direct assessment

The candidate must present logged evidence of at
least two season's sailing experience. He will
satisfactorily complete all of Section A and shall,
afloat and ashore, satisfactorily answer questions on
Section B. Candidates seeking assessment on
coastal waters will demonstrate knowledge of
Section C

Chief Instructor's signature

*Not necessarily applicable to keelboats

†Not necessarily applicable to multihulls

Day Sailing

On completion of this course, the successful sailor will have a confident, safe approach to planning and executing a short cruise in a dinghy/keelboat/multihull.

It is assumed that every student starting this course has already mastered the practical skills and absorbed the background knowledge required for *Basic Skills Level 2*. In addition, sailors wishing to cruise independently should ensure that they understand and can carry out the manoeuvres in the *Seamanship Skills* (see page 10) part of the National Sailing Scheme.

The course will be supervised by a Coastal Senior Instructor and will normally be conducted on coastal waters.

Tuition will be given by trained instructors, using appropriate supervision ratios with regard to the location and competence of the students. The course will include the planning and execution of a short cruise.

Students will be kept informed of their individual progress throughout the course.

Candidates who hold the RYA Day Skipper Shore Based Course Completion Certificate or a higher level RYA cruising award may gain exemption from the chartwork part of Section B.

Section A
Practical

Rigging
Can prepare and equip a boat for cruising including safety and navigation equipment, clothing and food
Can stow gear correctly

Instructor's signature

Sailing techniques and manoeuvres
Can plan and undertake a day sail including a consideration of pilotage/navigation and collision avoidance

Can use anchor to effect lee shore landing and departure*†

Instructor's signature

Adverse conditions
Is able to self rescue following total inversion*

Understands how to improvise in the event of gear failure

Instructor's signature

Section B
Sailing Background

Sailing theory and background
Has knowledge of boat handling in strong winds and difficult conditions (practical where possible)

Instructor's signature

Navigation

Can plan a day's cruise in coastal waters, including knowledge of:

Publications available particularly charts, tide tables, tidal stream atlases

Navigational instruments and their limitations afloat

Use of GPS including waypoint navigation. Confirming position by another source

Tidal heights and tidal streams (rule of twelfths or percentage rule), probable changes in the weather and the interaction of weather and tidal streams

Decision making in adverse circumstances including planning alternatives and refuges

Magnetic compass: variation and deviation

Interpretation of charts

Use of transits and bearings to steer course and fix position

Recording position and principles of dead reckoning

Instructor's signature

First aid

Has a basic knowledge of first aid - *those holding a valid first aid certificate are exempt from this item*

Instructor's signature

Meteorology

Knows sources of information on weather patterns for the day. Understands main characteristics of high and low pressure systems and simple interpretation of synoptic charts. Has awareness of changing weather conditions

Instructor's signature

Experienced sailor's direct assessment

The candidate must present logged evidence of at least two season's sailing experience. The candidate will complete all of Section A, demonstrating a competent, purposeful and safe approach. He will answer questions on Section B and wherever possible demonstrate skills satisfactorily afloat and ashore

Chief Instructor's signature

* Not necessarily applicable to keelboats

† Not necessarily applicable to multihulls

Sailing with Spinnakers

On completion of this course the successful sailor will understand how to sail a dinghy/keelboat/multihull rigged with an asymmetric or symmetric spinnaker. It is assumed that every student starting this course has already mastered the practical skills and absorbed the background knowledge required for *Basic Skills Level 2*.

Tuition will be given by an Advanced Instructor, or by an Instructor with appropriate experience approved by the Principal, using appropriate supervision ratios with regard to the location and competence of the students.

Students will be kept informed of their individual progress throughout the course.

Section A
Practical

Rigging
Can rig boats including spinnaker, and trapeze where fitted

Instructor's signature

Launching and recovery
Understands how to launch boats with open transoms and/or racks*†

Instructor's signature

Sailing techniques and manoeuvres
Can sail as crew or helm using equipment to good advantage

Can perform spinnaker hoist, gybe and drop as crew or helm

Understands and can sail best course downwind

Instructor's signature

Capsize recovery
Can perform capsize recovery including spinnaker
Knows how to recover from total inversion *

Instructor's signature

Section B
Sailing Background

Racing
Has knowledge of courses for type of boat

Instructor's signature

Sailing theory and background
Understands the concept of apparent wind sailing

Understands the effect of hull shape on performance

Can access sources of information and apply rig set-up for different conditions

Instructor's signature

Experienced sailor's direct assessment

The candidate will complete all of Section A, demonstrating a competent, purposeful and confident approach to an Advanced Instructor. He will satisfactorily answer questions on Section B afloat and ashore

* Not necessarily applicable to keelboats

† Not necessarily applicable to multihulls

Start Racing

This course is designed to give the confidence, skills and knowledge to take part in club racing in good conditions.

Confidence is essential if the sailor is to enjoy racing. The course involves the sailor in a range of enjoyable exercises designed to build confidence and to improve skills through practice.

It is assumed that every student starting this course has already mastered the practical skills and absorbed the background knowledge required for *Basic Skills Level 2.*

Tuition will be given by a Racing Instructor or a Club Racing Coach in dinghies, keelboats or multihulls.

Much or all of the work afloat will be done without an instructor on board, so the student to instructor ratio may be increased according to the conditions.

Students will be kept informed of their individual progress throughout the course.

Theory and background

General background
Insurance and measurement certificates

Choosing the right boat for you

> *Instructor's signature*

Race organisation
Handicap and One Design racing, Portsmouth Yardsticks

> *Instructor's signature*

The course and starting sequence
Simple sailing instructions for racing and typical courses

Starting systems 5-4-1-go, 10-5-go, 6-3-go

Flags, individual recall, general recall, shortened course

> *Instructor's signature*

Boat preparation
How to rig a racing dinghy

The availability of class tuning guides

> *Instructor's signature*

RYA *Membership*

Promoting and Protecting Boating
www.rya.org.uk

RYA Membership

Promoting and Protecting Boating

The RYA is the national organisation which represents the interests of everyone who goes boating for pleasure.

The greater the membership, the louder our voice when it comes to protecting members' interests.

Apply for membership today, and support the RYA, to help the RYA support you.

Benefits of Membership

- Access to expert advice on all aspects of boating from legal wrangles to training matters
- Special members' discounts on a range of products and services including boat insurance, books, videos and class certificates
- Free issue of certificates of competence, increasingly asked for by everyone from overseas governments to holiday companies, insurance underwriters to boat hirers

- Access to the wide range of RYA publications, including the quarterly magazine
- Third Party insurance for windsurfing members
- Free Internet access with RYA-Online
- Special discounts on AA membership
- Regular offers in RYA Magazine
- ...and much more

Join now - membership form opposite

Join online at www.rya.org.uk

Visit our website for information, advice, members' services and web shop.

1 Important To help us comply with Data Protection legislation, please tick *either* Box A or Box B (you must tick Box A to ensure you receive the full benefits of RYA membership). The RYA will not pass your data to third parties.

☐ **A.** I wish to join the RYA and receive future information on member services, benefits (as listed in RYA Magazine and website) and offers.

☐ **B.** I wish to join the RYA but do not wish to receive future information on member services, benefits (as listed in RYA Magazine and website) and offers.

When completed, please send this form to: RYA, RYA House, Ensign Way, Hamble, Southampton, SO31 4YA

2

Title	Forename	Surname	Date of Birth		Male	Female
			D D / M M / Y Y		☐	☐
1.			D D / M M / Y Y		☐	☐
2.			D D / M M / Y Y		☐	☐
3.			D D / M M / Y Y		☐	☐
4.						

Address

Town **County** **Post Code**

Evening Telephone **Daytime Telephone**

email

3 Type of membership required: *(Tick Box)*

☐ **Personal** *Before 1 October 2005 annual rate £33 or £30 by Direct Debit*
From 1 October 2005 annual rate £37 or £34 by Direct Debit

☐ **Under 21** *Before 1 October 2005 annual rate £11 (no reduction for Direct Debit)*
From 1 October 2005 annual rate £12 (no reduction for Direct Debit)

☐ **Family*** *Before 1 October 2005 annual rate £50 or £47 by Direct Debit*
From 1 October 2005 annual rate £56 or £52 by Direct Debit

* *Family Membership: 2 adults plus any under 21s all living at the same address*

Signature: _____ **Date:** _____

4 Please tick ONE box to show your main boating interest.

☐ Yacht Racing ☐ Yacht Cruising
☐ Dinghy Racing ☐ Dinghy Cruising
☐ Personal Watercraft ☐ Inland Waterways
☐ Powerboat Racing ☐ Windsurfing
☐ Motor Boating ☐ Sportsboats and RIBs

Please see Direct Debit form overleaf

Instructions to your Bank or Building Society to pay by Direct Debit

Please complete this form and return it to:
Royal Yachting Association, RYA House, Ensign Way, Hamble, Southampton, Hampshire SO31 4YA

DIRECT Debit

Originators Identification Number

9	5	5	2	1	3

5. RYA Membership Number (For office use only)

To The Manager: _____ Bank/Building Society

Address: _____

_____

Post Code: _____

2. Name(s) of account holder(s)

3. Branch Sort Code

4. Bank or Building Society account number

Banks and Building Societies may not accept Direct Debit instructions for some types of account

6. Instruction to pay your Bank or Building Society

Please pay Royal Yachting Association Direct Debits from the account detailed in this instruction subject to the safeguards assured by The Direct Debit Guarantee.
I understand that this instruction may remain with the Royal Yachting Association and, if so, details will be passed electronically to my Bank/Building Society.

Signature(s) _____

Date _____

Office use / Centre Stamp

Cash, Cheque, Postal Order enclosed £ _____
Made payable to the Royal Yachting Association

Office use only: Membership Number Allocated

077

Boat tuning

How to alter sail controls around the course and in
different conditions

Boat handling

How to make best use of the Five Essentials when
racing, as helm or crew

How to round marks

Pre-start boat handling at slow speed including
starting and stopping

How to right the boat after a capsize*

Multihulls only - how to apply the principles of crew
weight, airflow, technique (C.A.T)

Starting

Use of transits - where am I?

Choosing the right end of the line - reaching along
line or head to wind

Clear wind with speed on the line at gun with gap
to leeward

Involving the crew to best effect

Race strategy

Sailing upwind

Clear air, gusts and lulls

Headers and lifts, use of telltales

The effect of geography around the course

The effect of tidal flow

Sailing downwind

Reaching and running, choosing the fastest course

Finishing

How to pick the right end of the line

Tactics

When boats meet - boat on boat tactics

Racing rules

Introduction to the *Racing Rules of Sailing*, including the Fundamental Rules (Part 1).

Awareness of the definitions of *keeping clear, proper course and room*, with the aim of getting around the course and avoiding a collision while sailing fairly.

When boats meet:

Port and starboard

Windward boat

Two boat lengths at marks, including gybe

Overlaps

Penalties

Practical exercises

Training exercises should form a large part of the course. These should include:

Starting practice

Windward leeward courses

Triangle courses

Mark rounding

Piggy in the middle

Bungee on the tiller

Holding position (before start)

Tacking on the whistle

Sailors should be encouraged to practice informally following the course.

* Not necessarily applicable to keelboats

† Not necessarily applicable to multihulls

Performance Sailing

On completion of this course, the successful sailor will understand how to sail performance dinghies/keelboats/multihulls in all wind conditions that they can expect to encounter, sailing the boat to best advantage at all times.

The emphasis is on coaching to improve the candidate's sailing performance. This will involve coaching from powerboats.

This course is intended primarily for two-person spinnaker boats. However, it may be delivered in performance singlehanders and the certificate endorsed accordingly.

Tuition will be given by an Advanced Instructor for the type of boat, using appropriate supervision ratios with regard to the location and competence of the students and the need to provide continuous feedback on the water.

It is assumed that every student starting this course has already mastered the practical skills and absorbed the background knowledge required for *Basic Skills Level 2*. In practical terms, at least a full season's sailing experience since learning to sail is advisable.

Students will be kept informed of their individual progress throughout the course.

Section A
Practical

Rigging
Can rig any type of boat, including spinnaker and trapeze (if fitted)

Instructor's signature

Sailing techniques and manoeuvres
Can make best possible use of crew and equipment to sail efficiently on all points of sailing in a variety of conditions, including symmetric or asymmetric spinnaker

Can spot and use windshifts and gusts to effect best course up and down wind

Can perform capsize recovery including spinnaker. Knows how to recover from total inversion*

Instructor's signature

Section B
Sailing Background

Sailing theory and background
Understands how to make use of wind variation and tidal eddies which occur due to geographical features and tidal conditions

Has an understanding of hull shapes and rig types, including their effect on performance

Understands planing and the effect of rails

Instructor's signature

Meteorology

Knows sources of information on weather patterns for the day. Understands main characteristics of high and low pressure systems and simple interpretation of synoptic charts. Has awareness of changing weather conditions

Instructor's signature

Experienced sailor's direct assessment

The candidate must present logged evidence of at least two season's sailing experience. The candidate will complete all of Section A, demonstrating a competent, purposeful and safe approach to sailing performance boats. He will answer questions on Section B afloat and ashore

Chief Instructor's signature

* Not applicable to keelboats

Personal log

Date	Type of Boat	Hours Experience		Activity and Weather Conditions		Authorisation
		Helmsman	Crew	Type of Course or activity	Max Wind Speed	Centre/Club Instructor
March/ April 98	GP14	12		Spring Series	F5	Southport SC H. Potter

Personal log

Date	Type of Boat	Hours Experience		Activity and Weather Conditions		Authorisation
		Helmsman	Crew	Type of Course or activity	Max Wind Speed	Centre/Club Instructor

Personal log

Date	Type of Boat	Hours Experience		Activity and Weather Conditions		Authorisation
		Helmsman	Crew	Type of Course or activity	Max Wind Speed	Centre/Club Instructor

24

Start Sailing - Level 1

D11

RYA National Sailing Scheme

PLEASE ATTACH YOUR RYA CERTIFICATE HERE

Please note that no record
of certificates is held by the RYA

Enquiries about lost certificates
should be made to the centre
where the course was taken

RYA

Basic Skills - Level 2

PLEASE ATTACH YOUR RYA CERTIFICATE HERE

Please note that no record
of certificates is held by the RYA

Enquiries about lost certificates
should be made to the centre
where the course was taken

RYA

Seamanship Skills

RYA National Sailing Scheme

PLEASE ATTACH YOUR RYA CERTIFICATE HERE

Please note that no record
of certificates is held by the RYA

Enquiries about lost certificates
should be made to the centre
where the course was taken

Day Sailing

PLEASE ATTACH YOUR RYA CERTIFICATE HERE

Please note that no record
of certificates is held by the RYA

Enquiries about lost certificates
should be made to the centre
where the course was taken

Sailing with
Spinnakers

RYA National Sailing Scheme

D15

Start Racing

D16

PLEASE ATTACH YOUR RYA CERTIFICATE HERE

Please note that no record
of certificates is held by the RYA

Enquiries about lost certificates
should be made to the centre
where the course was taken

PLEASE ATTACH YOUR RYA CERTIFICATE HERE

Please note that no record
of certificates is held by the RYA

Enquiries about lost certificates
should be made to the centre
where the course was taken

RYA National Sailing Scheme

RYA Sailability
Awareness Training Course

PLEASE ATTACH YOUR RYA CERTIFICATE HERE

Please note that no record
of certificates is held by the RYA

Enquiries about lost certificates
should be made to the centre
where the course was taken

RYA Sailability
Volunteer Management

PLEASE ATTACH YOUR RYA CERTIFICATE HERE

Please note that no record
of certificates is held by the RYA

Enquiries about lost certificates
should be made to the centre
where the course was taken